Natural
Environment
Research
Council

Institute of Terrestrial Ecology

Climatic change, rising sea level and the British coast

ITE research publication no. 1

L A Boorman
J D Goss-Custard
S McGrorty

London : Her Majesty's Stationery Office

CW00969494

COVER ILLUSTRATIONS (L A Boorman)
Clockwise order:
Upper general salt marsh dominated by flowering sea lavender
Rough sea at Lindesfarne, Northumberland
Shingle beach with vegetation along the lows, Culbin, Nairn, Highland Region
Bulcamp Marshes, River Blythe, Southwold, Suffolk
Sandy beach and dunes, Newton Links, Northumberland
Sand dunes and dune slacks, Whiteford, Glamorgan

The INSTITUTE OF TERRESTRIAL ECOLOGY (ITE) is one of 15 component and grant-aided research organizations within the NATURAL ENVIRONMENT RESEARCH COUNCIL. The Institute is part of the Terrestrial and Freshwater Sciences Directorate, and was established in 1973 by the merger of the research stations of the Nature Conservancy with the Institute of Tree Biology. It has been at the forefront of ecological research ever since. The six research stations of the Institute provide a ready access to sites and to environmental and ecological problems in any part of Britain. In addition to the broad environmental knowledge and experience expected of the modern ecologist, each station has a range of special expertise and facilities. Thus, the Institute is able to provide unparalleled opportunities for long-term multidisciplinary studies of complex environmental and ecological problems.

ITE undertakes specialist ecological research on subjects ranging from micro-organisms to trees and mammals, from coastal habitats to uplands, from derelict land to air pollution. Understanding the ecology of different species of natural and man-made communities plays an increasingly important role in areas such as improving productivity in forestry, rehabilitating disturbed sites, monitoring the effects of pollution, managing and conserving wildlife, and controlling pests.

The Institute's research is financed by the UK Government through the science budget, and by private and public sector customers who commission or sponsor specific research programmes. ITE's expertise is also widely used by international organizations in overseas collaborative projects.

The results of ITE research are available to those responsible for the protection, management and wise use of our natural resources, being published in a wide range of scientific journals, and in an ITE series of publications. The Annual Report contains more general information.

This report was jointly commissioned by the Department of the Environment and the Natural Environment Research Council as one of a series of six reviews assessing the possible impact of climatic change on various sectors of the natural environment. The views expressed and the conclusions reached are those of the authors, and should not be regarded as representing the policy of either the Department of Environment or the Natural Environment Research Council.

Dr L A Boorman
Institute of Terrestrial Ecology
Monks Wood Experimental Station
Abbots Ripton
Huntingdon
PE17 2LS
Tel: 04873 381

Contents

CONTENTS

Illustrations

Plate 1 (3)   An example of a protected coast at Frinton, Essex,
where soft earth cliffs are protected by a sea wall and groynes.
(Photograph L A Boorman)

Plate 2 (5.1)   Pioneer cordgrass *(Spartina anglica)* at Hamford Water, Essex.
The exposed roots show some erosion taking place.
(Photograph L A Boorman)

Plate 3 (5.1)   Salt marsh vegetation at Hamford Water, Essex.
The main vegetation is dominated by sea aster *(Aster tripolium)*,
the creek sides, being lower, have stands of marsh samphire *(Salicornia europaea* agg.*)* and the higher marsh in the right foreground and
middle distance has sea lavender *(Limonium vulgare)* and sea purslane
(Halimione portulacoides).
(Photograph L A Boorman)

Plate 4 (5.1)   Eroded salt marsh at Hamford Water, Essex.
The bare mud bank was formerly stabilized by salt marsh and is high
enough to support vegetation, but it remains bare.
(Photograph L A Boorman)

Plate 5 (7)   Brent geese *(Brenta bernicla)* at Leigh Marsh, Essex.
(Photograph K Charman)

Plate 6 (7)   Sea grass *(Zostera marina),* the food of the brent goose.
(Photograph K Charman)

Plate 7 (8.3)   Active mobile sand dunes on both sides of the mouth of the
River Ythan, Aberdeenshire.
(Photograph L A Boorman)

Plate 8 (8.4)   The shingle bank at Walberswick, Suffolk,
is being forced shorewards over the salt marshes behind.
(Photograph L A Boorman)

Plate 9 (9.1)   Soft cliffs of glacial sand and gravel at Mundesley, Norfolk,
are readily eroded by the sea.
(Photograph L A Boorman)

Plate 10 (10)   Hickling Broad, Norfolk.
There is already a detectable marine influence in some of the eastern
broads, of which Hickling is typical.
(Photograph L A Boorman)

Executive summary

1. Introduction
Most experts agree that, if the present trends continue, the concentration of atmospheric CO_2 will have doubled by the year 2050. This increase will have an important effect on the world's climate, with a marked rise in temperature globally. Much of England would experience a climate similar to the present climate of south-west France.

2. The sea level change scenario
It is predicted that this global warming will cause large rises in sea level. There have been several forecasts of sea level rises of at least one metre in the next hundred years and there have been predictions of rises of as great as 4 m. This report considers the biological implications of sea level rises of 0.8 m up to 1.65 m in 100 years.

3. Changes in sea defence and coast protection
It has been estimated that the improvement of existing sea defences to withstand such a rise in sea level would cost at least £5,000,000,000. Various options for sea defence and coastal protection would have to be considered, including raising the existing sea walls, building new walls further inland, building storm surge barriers, building major estuarine barrages, and even abandoning whole sections of coast.

4. Changes on soft coasts with sea walls
The greatest impact of such a rise in sea level would be on soft coasts protected by sea walls. As the sea rises, erosive processes would become dominant and there would be considerable losses, especially of fine sediments, although there would be partial re-deposition in sheltered areas. The slope of the shore would become steeper and each zone narrower. The sea wall would have to withstand increased erosive forces following the loss of the salt marshes, mud flats and sandy beaches to seawards.

It is estimated for Essex, for example, that a sea level rise of 0.8 m could lead to the loss of the present upper marsh by reversion to lower marsh and a reduction of at least 20% in the area of mud flats; any rise greater than about one metre could lead to a near total loss of marsh and a reduction of 30–50% in the area of mud flats.

The invertebrate fauna of the intertidal flats would become poorer and less diverse, except locally in fine sediments. The productivity of the surviving species would be reduced by the high loads of suspended sediments in the inshore waters. These changes would greatly reduce the large numbers of the many species of birds that roost, feed or breed in the area. At present,

British estuaries are the wintering ground for more than one half of Europe's waders. Salt marshes provide the breeding habitat for a number of species – 60% of British redshank nest in the salt marshes.

5. New sea walls further inland
If new sea walls were to be built further inland, there should be a partial regeneration of existing habitats, but this would involve the loss of agricultural land as well as some habitats of conservation interest inside the sea wall. This regeneration of habitats would require that sea walls be relocated a substantial distance landwards for there to be a full replacement of lost habitats.

6. Storm surge barriers
A partial (storm surge) barrier would increase sedimentation inside the barrier, which would tend to favour the growth of salt marsh at the expense of mud flats. The intertidal invertebrates would remain for a while before the habitat was lost to salt marsh or by the drying out of the surface. The number of birds able to use the area would be reduced because of a loss of food resources within the mud flats.

7. Tidal barrages
An impermeable barrier excluding the sea completely would cause the total loss of the existing fauna and flora. A range of new fresh water habitats, open water, marsh and grassland would develop.

8. Effects on other coastal habitats
There would also be considerable changes in most other coastal areas, affecting sand dunes, shingle banks and earth cliffs. Unless unrestrained landward movement was possible, increased erosion would cause extensive losses. Changes inland would include increased flooding both by the sea and by fresh water, and considerable extra penetration of salt water directly up the rivers and indirectly through the groundwater.

9. Socio-economic implications
It is ironic that many of the existing holiday beaches would disappear just as the climate was becoming similar to that of present-day Biarritz. Recreational pressure would thus increase on the limited areas still available.

10. Strategy for action
Coastal resources and coastal processes are still only partly understood, especially in relation to the changes that rising sea levels would cause. We cannot plan effectively for the conservation and management of our coastal resources without further research on several key points. Action is necessary to reconcile the conflicting demands on our threatened coastal resources.

FIGURE 1. Areas of Great Britain vulnerable to a rising sea level

Introduction

One of the more dramatic consequences that can be expected from a global warming is a rise in mean sea level. The consensus of opinion is that, over the past century, mean sea level has risen by some 10–15 cm (Robin 1986), although in many parts of the world this rise is obscured by vertical land movements (Pirazzoli 1986). The rising temperatures affect the sea level in several different ways; these include the direct thermal expansion of the oceans, the melting of glacier ice, and the melting of polar ice sheets. Only the first-mentioned process, the thermal expansion of the oceans, has been modelled effectively, but opinions differ as to the relative significance of the various processes contributing to the sea level rise.

The net result is a wide variation in the forecasts of sea level changes over the next century or so. Estimates vary from 0.5 m up to an extreme of 3.5 m (Hoffman 1984). A recent Dutch study postulates a probable rise of 1 m in the next 100 years and a possible rise of 5 m in 200 years (Anon 1986). Similar or even higher predictions have also been made for this country (a rise of up to 4.5 m in less than 50 years has been predicted for the Wash – I Shennan, pers. comm.). Something approaching a consensus view is provided by Robin (1986), with a middle estimate of 0.80 m and a maximum of 1.65 m. These figures will be taken as the core scenario for the purposes of this publication.

The general eustatic rise in sea level is not the whole story. In Britain, the areas of coast most susceptible to rises in sea level lie in the south-east of the island, just the areas that are sinking relative to the sea as a result of isostatic adjustment. Estimates of this process vary, but they could be in the order of 3 mm per year (Butler 1978). Second, climatic changes themselves would have a direct effect on at least some of the species, communities and ecosystems on the coast. Finally, a recent report has suggested that the north-east Atlantic has become notably rougher over the past 25 years (Carter & Draper 1988), which would significantly increase the impact of a rise in sea level, especially on exposed coasts.

Sea level is not a constant factor but is subject to complex cyclic (tidal) and non-cyclic fluctuations (eg changes due to variations in barometric pressure, changes due to wind, ie storm surges, etc). The changes in tidal range (difference in level between mean high water spring tides and mean low water spring tides) around Britain vary from as little as 2 m in open water and along the east Norfolk coast up to 11 m and more in semi-enclosed areas such as the Severn estuary. The range increases up the estuary to a maximum, after which the tidal influence progressively

decreases, although some effects can still be detected at very considerable distances from the sea.

The effect of a rise in sea level on tidal regimes is not a simple one, as the various components that make up the tide are affected differently. While a first approximation can be made by simply adding the sea level rise, as a constant, to the tidal curves, recent studies in the Bay of Bengal (Flather & Khandker 1987) have shown the need for model studies to define the changes accurately. The studies showed that both tidal amplitude and storm surges could be increased and decreased at different points in an estuary following a rise in sea level. The magnitude was relatively small, but by no means insignificant (tidal amplitude +6% to −8%, tide + surge elevation +12% to −25%). However, these results are from a preliminary study of one particular site and can only be taken as indicating the need for detailed studies of specific cases.

A factor omitted in the Bengal study was the influence of river flow. The core scenario for this study includes the possibility of an increase in rainfall of 20%. Such an increase could clearly have some effect on river discharge which, if coincident with tidal or surge flooding, could be important.

The coastline of Britain can be subdivided into two categories, the mainly low-lying soft coasts, often protected by a sea wall, and the harder, predominantly cliff, coasts. The cliff coasts associated with harder rocks in the north and west would be little affected, even with a sea level rise of some magnitude, although there are sheltered inlets with salt marsh, shingle and sand dune communities. However, in the absence of artificial restraints, these isolated communities and ecosystems would probably adjust to rising sea levels by slowly migrating landwards. Difficulties could arise if these natural changes came into conflict with man-made structures or agricultural activities. This report concentrates on the effects of sea level rise on the soft coast, both the large areas of soft coast in the south-east and elsewhere and on the small, more or less isolated, areas of soft coast that occur all round the British Isles.

A rise in sea level would result in increased erosion, but such erosion can usually release enough sediments into circulation to allow the coast to reform more or less unchanged, the classic 'sea level transgression'. These processes are illustrated by the barrier island coasts found in north Norfolk, or, especially, the north of the Netherlands and north Germany. The development of new marshes and mud flats is, however, a slow process, and it is possible that the rate of sea level rise might be too great for these natural processes of recovery to take place. In addition, these processes depend on there being no artificial barriers to limit the advance of the sea landwards.

Along nearly all of the low-lying coasts of Britain this transgression process is inhibited by the existence of sea walls that protect life and property against any intrusion of the sea. A rise in sea level would increase the rate of erosion of marshes seawards of the sea wall, and the sediment would generally be lost from the immediate system. However, most of the sea walls are composed of erodable material and are lightly protected against erosion. They are generally only high enough to give protection against present sea levels. A sea level rise of the magnitude postulated would require a major review of sea defence and coast protection policies. The effect of sea level rise on coastal ecosystems would thus depend considerably on the choice of options for sea defence (Section 3) and their implications (Section 4). Only then can consideration be given to the effect of sea level rise on the vegetation of mud flats and salt marshes (Section 5), on the populations of the invertebrates of the mud flats (Section 6), and on the bird populations associated with these habitats (Section 7).

Some parts of these low-lying coasts are fronted and protected by sand dunes or shingle banks. These areas would also be vulnerable to change as a result of a rise in sea level, especially where there is insufficient space for them to reform landwards (Section 8).

Sea level rise would also present a significant problem, however, in those areas with a cliff coast where the cliffs are composed of softer rocks, such as the 'earth' cliffs of north Humberside and parts of Norfolk and Suffolk (Section 9). The present, not inconsiderable, rates of erosion would be dramatically enhanced. If erosion was allowed to proceed unchecked, then there would be a substantial enhancement of the supplies of sediment to salt marsh and sand dune areas further along the coast. Conversely, the prevention of erosion would cut off this supply of sand and sediment and could result in increased erosion elsewhere.

In addition to the direct effect already mentioned, a rise in sea level would affect areas some distance inland. There is likely to be increased flooding in coastal areas by sea water or brackish water, and salt penetration of the groundwater would increase further inland (Salinas, Delaune & Patrick 1986). There would also be a more marked and more frequent penetration of salt water upstream, such as occurred in the Norfolk Broads early in 1988 resulting in the dramatic fish kill. There could also be effects far inland as a result of new sea defence strategies (Section 10).

All parts of the coast of the British Isles would be affected by a rise in sea level of the degree predicted. The magnitude of these effects would vary greatly on a regional basis (Section 11).

There are many conflicting demands on our coastal resources. Sea level rise will thus have considerable socio-economic implications (Section 12).

The effects of sea level rise on all coastal ecosystems are likely to be considerable, and potentially catastrophic for some of them. Deleterious changes could be offset to a considerable degree by appropriate management soundly based on research (Section 13).

Sea level change and sea defence options

In the past, small rises in sea level have been provided for, and factors of safety against storm surges have been increased mainly by raising the height of existing structures, although these actions have been supplemented by major projects, such as the Thames barrier. The magnitude of the rises postulated, however, pose radically different problems. It appears that many existing sea walls lack the foundations to withstand raising them by the required amount. Even if such a measure were possible, it would cost between £2,500 and £3,000 per metre to raise the walls sufficiently to cope with a rise of 1.65 m (A J Allison, pers. comm.). This estimate makes no allowance for secondary climatic effects, such as the deteriorating wave climate, which could make the situation worse.

In addition to the costs of raising existing sea defences, there is also the problem of the various outfalls. The vast majority of gravity outfalls would become inoperable, and many pumping stations would have to be modified or replaced at an estimated cost of £2,000 M.

With an estimated total capital cost of £5,000 M for replacing the sea defences, by conventional means, to cope with a sea level rise of 1.65 m by the year 2050 (A J Allison, pers. comm.), some areas might have to be abandoned and left unprotected because the works could not be justified from cost benefit considerations,

while other areas might have to be protected in ways different from today. Major estuaries could be protected with barriers, but generally this would involve expenditure at least as great as that of raising present sea walls. An alternative is to abandon some land and reconstruct the sea wall landwards. The abandoned land would then form new saltings that would give extra protection to the sea wall. The wall would thus cost less to construct than an exposed sea wall but, to this figure, would have to be added the cost of acquiring the agricultural land that would be abandoned.

Given the predicted rises in sea level, it seems likely that the tactical outcome would represent a combination of these various approaches. Certain options may be inherently more expensive but might have other cost benefits, eg barrages for sea defence and tidal power. Environmental consideration will, therefore, be given to these four distinct options, together with the ultimate alternative of abandoning the coast:

(a) Present sea walls raised
(b) New sea walls constructed landwards of existing ones
(c) Storm surge barriers built across estuaries
(d) Impermeable barriers built across estuaries
(e) Abandonment of coast

An example of a protected coast at Frinton, Essex, where soft earth cliffs are protected by a sea wall and groynes

General effects of the various options

4.1 Introduction

The effects would vary depending on whether the shoreline is primarily open tidal flats or a large estuary, or whether it is in the form of an estuary well protected by a narrow entrance. In an open situation, the increase in water level and higher wave energy would result in increased erosion and increased sediment instability. The fine sediments would probably be deposited elsewhere or offshore and might be lost to the system, at least locally. The increased wave energy would also cause the sediments to be reworked, with a removal of fines and an increase in coarse sediments. The effective levels of the flats would decrease as a result of both sea level rise and erosion. In some cases, underlying harder sediments would be exposed. It is also possible that the shore profile would become more concave so that the length of exposure at low tide would decrease.

The situation would be rather different for a sheltered estuary or inlet. With the protection from vigorous wave action, the increase in sediment supply could lead to a marked increase in accretion, at least locally. On the flats, fine sediments would continue to predominate. However, at some stage, sand dunes, sand bars or shingle banks could be overtopped, resulting in the mouth of the estuary being widened and protection decreased. In this case, the erosional trends predicted for the open shore would also occur in these estuaries and inlets.

4.2 Present sea walls raised

The rise in water level would result in increased erosion in all but the most sheltered areas. The shoreline would become steeper and narrower, and sediments generally coarser. Fine sediments would tend to be lost to the system, although locally they would move to the more sheltered areas.

4.3 New sea walls constructed landwards

If the new sea walls were built sufficiently far inland, the shore would simply migrate landwards and the habitats would remain much the same as at present. The distance required would vary greatly. In some cases, it would be to the start of higher ground. In the case of a low-lying coast, as in much of Essex, the necessary distance could only be determined by detailed studies to find the point at which a new equilibrium would be reached between the higher sea level and the increased shelter and increased sediment supply as a result of moving landwards. In some areas, especially around the Wash, it would appear that levels inside the present sea wall are rather too low for this approach to be effective. If the new sea walls were not constructed sufficiently far inland, for the full regeneration of present habitats, the results would be similar to those detailed in Section 4.1 but less marked.

4.4 Storm surge barriers built across estuaries

Storm surge barriers work by cutting off extreme high tides. The frequency with which restriction would occur would depend on the operational policy selected, but, in general, the overall result would be a reduction in tidal range and a longer period of slack water at high tide, which would tend to increase sedimentation, especially at the higher vegetated levels. The resulting growth of salt marsh would lead to a narrowing of the width of the intertidal mud flats, which would tend to be composed of finer sediments. There would also be an increase in the silting up of the channels and creeks.

4.5 Impermeable barriers built across estuaries

Such barriers would isolate the area from marine influences and create fresh water lakes, marshes and grassland, with a whole range of new non-saline habitats, thus bringing about a complete change in the ecology of the area.

4.6 Abandonment of coast

If all forms of sea defence or coast protection were abandoned, then the classic 'transgression' would occur, as already described. Erosion would take place until a new stability was reached, with sediments moving inshore and being redeposited. In general, existing habitats would be reformed and, in some cases, even extended in area, with a reversion to the situation that existed before the sea walls were built. It would take many years for existing salt marshes and mud flats to be eroded, and there would, therefore, be a lag period before a new equilibrium was reached.

Changes in mud flat and salt marsh vegetation

5.1 Distribution of salt marsh vegetation

The vegetation of salt marshes and vegetated mud flats occurs in distinct zones related to the tidal regime, to the periods of submersion or emergence that the component plant species can withstand. Intertidal flats can have transient communities of algae, even at the lower levels. Mud flats generally only support vascular (higher) plants when they are exposed for longer periods than they are covered by the sea.

Vegetation thus starts at a level rather above mean sea level. Typically, at the lowest levels, the mud flats only have scattered stands of seagrass (Zostera spp.). This plant is, however, really marine rather than terrestrial, as many other species of Zostera can grow permanently submerged.

The primary colonizer of the lower flats is usually marsh samphire (Salicornia spp.), first as scattered individuals, then as dense stands. In certain areas, however, the pioneer species is the alien hybrid cordgrass (Spartina anglica). Locally, it has come to dominate vast areas, but recently it has decreased considerably in its extent and distribution, particularly in the south-east of Britain.

The marshes above the pioneer zone have a lower zone dominated by sea aster (Aster tripolium) and marsh samphire, and an upper zone dominated by a range of species, including sea meadow grass (Puccinellia maritima), sea lavender (Limonium vulgare), and sea purslane (Halimione portulacoides), the so-called general salt marsh (GSM). The lower marsh is covered by every tide, while the upper GSM is only covered by the higher spring tides. Between the GSM and the lower marsh, there is often a distinctive intermediate zone, dominated by sea meadow grass and sea purslane.

The GSM itself can usually be divided into an upper and lower zone, based on the occurrence of species like sea thrift (Armeria maritima). This upper zone is only covered by the highest tides. The upper edge of the salt marsh can be recognized by the occurrence of sea couch-grass (Elymus pycnanthus) along the line reached by the highest (equinoctial) spring tides.

This example is a considerable simplification, as many plant species and plant communities are involved (Beeftink 1979). The simple examples given above will, however, serve to demonstrate the principles and processes.

Each zone can be defined in terms of the tidal regime that the component plant species can tolerate at critical stages in their life cycle. In the normal situation, the surface of the marsh is built up by the accretion of sediment. The vegetation, by slowing the water flow, traps the sediment. The plant cover and the plant roots help to protect the substrate from erosion. As accretion proceeds and the surface of the marsh builds up, the first colonizers, more tolerant of submersion but less vigorously competitive, are progressively replaced, in a regular sequence of species and communities.

The pioneer stands of marsh samphire are replaced by low marsh with mixed communities, dominated first by sea aster and marsh samphire, and then by sea meadow grass and sea purslane, and ultimately by sea lavender and the other species of the GSM. If the sea level rises, however, there is a reversion to an earlier stage. The sequence of plant communities can then be repeated. The old marsh is recolonized by pioneer or

Pioneer cordgrass (Spartina anglica) at Hamford Water, Essex. The exposed roots show some erosion taking place

Salt marsh vegetation at Hamford Water, Essex. The main vegetation is dominated by sea aster (Aster tripolium), the creek sides, being lower, have stands of marsh samphire (Salicornia europaea agg.) and the higher marsh in the right foreground and middle distance has sea lavender (Limonium vulgare) and sea purslane (Halimione portulacoides)

early species and communities. This response to rising sea levels has partly been illustrated by the effects of the modified tidal regimes created by the Dutch Delta Works (Beeftink 1979; Groenendijk 1983, 1985). It must be noted that recovery is slow and there is an increased risk of erosion.

Salt marsh vegetation is affected directly by sea level rise by more frequent and longer submersion, and indirectly through the more severe wave climate that the marshes would experience because of the deeper water seawards. It is possible to estimate the direct effects of sea level rise much more accurately than the effects of a change in the wave climate and the associated increase in erosive processes.

Salt marshes are typically dynamic communities maintained by a balance between erosion and deposition, as has been shown by studies on the marshes of north Kent. As some areas of marsh were lost by erosion, the loss was offset by the growth of new marshes elsewhere (Kirby 1969). Recently, however, in the Essex area, there has been a tendency for erosive processes to become dominant, with extensive losses, especially of the lower zones of the salt marsh dominated by marsh samphire and sea aster (Boorman 1987). There are indications that this situation may also be occurring in various other parts of the south and south-east of Britain.

5.2   Changes on open coasts and large estuaries

In addition to the progressive drowning of the zones as the sea level rises, there would be an increase in the magnitude of erosive processes. Salt marsh edges would become cliffed, or existing cliffs would become more marked. The creek system would become rejuvenated and the creeks steeper and wider, with a

Eroded salt marsh at Hamford Water, Essex. The bare mud bank was formerly stablized by salt marsh and is high enough to support vegetation, but it remains bare

corresponding decrease in the area of the marsh covered by vegetation. Rates of accretion would tend to remain the same or even to decrease, except locally where there is some form of shelter, giving a further net loss of vegetated marsh.

5.3   Changes in narrow protected estuaries

In sheltered estuaries, the effect of the rise in sea level drowning the lower zone of vegetation would tend to be ameliorated by the increased availability of fine sediment, and thus the possibility of increased rates of sedimentation. It is difficult at present to quantify the magnitude of such an effect. It seems unlikely that there would be enough accretion anywhere to offset the sea level rise completely, except possibly at a very local scale. The normal upper limit of salt marsh growth, at around 10–20 mm per year, is close to the higher predicted rate of sea level rise (16.5 mm yr[-1]). However, the rejuvenated low marsh would generally receive sufficient sediment to enable some upward growth, and to allow for the possible regeneration of higher marsh. Salt marshes are known to act as sinks for pollutants, and sediment released by marsh erosion, when redeposited, may well not be favourable for plant growth. The growth of marsh in such a situation would inevitably mean a reduction in the extent of mud flats and a steepening of the lower shore.

5.4   Present sea walls raised

The effect of sea level rise on salt marsh vegetation can be illustrated by reference to the marshes of Dengie, Essex. Here, along a 12 km stretch of coast, a system of marshes and mud flats extends some 2 km seawards. While there is some variation along the length of the system, there is sufficient uniformity to define the zones in terms of mean width. In 1974, the GSM was 390 m wide, amounting to 470 ha; the lower marsh, dominated by sea aster and marsh samphire, 38 m (46 ha); the sea grass zone 70 m wide (84 ha); and 1570 m of mud flats (1900 ha). Present widths and areas of marsh are at least 10% less than those figures (Harmsworth & Long 1986). It must be noted that the estimates presented here do not include large-scale erosional changes that would also take place.

A sea level rise of 0.8 m would result in the upward displacement of each zone, with a near complete loss of the GSM. There would be a ten-fold increase in the lower marsh, to around 500 ha, and a slight decrease in the seagrass (50 ha). It has already been noted in Section 5.3 that, at present, the lower marsh communities in the Essex area are experiencing serious dieback and erosion, so that the stability of the 'secondary' lower marsh that would be formed cannot be taken for granted. The lowest areas of the mud flats would be lost, with very little compensatory gains from the former seagrass zone. Overall, the area of mud flats would fall by about 20%, from around 1900 ha to no more than 1300 ha. This estimate is likely to be the maximum figure and could be considerably decreased by the loss of fine sediment.

A sea level rise of 1.0 m is unlikely to have many extra effects on the marshes, although the extent of seagrass would probably be reduced to perhaps 40 ha. There would, however, be a significant decrease in the width of the mud flats, reducing in area to perhaps 1200 ha, 35% of its present area.

A sea level rise of 1.65 m would have dramatic effects, as the whole of the present marsh area would be too low for the growth of marsh vegetation, except for local fragments of pioneer species. In addition, there would be a loss of at least 50% of the mud flats. Only the seagrass might remain, if it was able to re-establish in its new position. Effectively, the new sea wall would be very exposed, completely unprotected by salt marshes.

It should be noted that, once the sea level rises much over about 1 m above its present level, the effects on the vegetation would become dramatic, with a near-total loss of salt marsh vegetation outside the sea wall. The exception would be those areas which have a greatly enhanced tidal range and a correspondingly wide amplitude in marsh vegetation. Here, the marsh losses would not be as great as in those areas with a small tidal range and narrow amplitude in marsh vegetation.

5.5 New sea walls constructed landwards

The effect of reconstructing the sea walls inland is much more difficult to quantify, particularly where, as in parts of Essex, there are areas of reclaimed land, formerly salt marsh, extending many miles inland. Certainly, there would be a point at which the present extent of salt marshes and mud flats could be regenerated, but it would involve the loss of fairly large areas of agricultural land. There could also be a significant loss of land devoted to conservation and amenity purposes.

While the areas of rough grazing marshes of high biological interest could probably be recreated from agricultural land, it would involve considerable expense, both in habitat creation research and in land purchase and land management.

5.6 Storm surge barriers built across estuaries

The ordinary rise in sea level would have substantially the same effects as outlined in Section 5.1. The longer slack period at high water would increase the opportunities for sedimentation, with a corresponding increase in salt marsh growth. It is likely that at least some of the areas of lower marsh formed from drowned GSM would build up into new high marsh. This marsh growth could, however, further decrease the loss of mud flats. The mud flats themselves would tend to retain fine sediments, with the increase in shelter.

5.7 Impermeable barriers built across estuaries

A sudden cessation of regular tidal submersions causes the disappearance of the original vegetation within 1–5 years (Beeftink 1979). The salt marsh vegetation is then succeeded by marshes and grassland, the nature of which is dependent on the grazing management. There is often a period of years in which weedy species are dominant, and a range of fresh water communities will also develop. The principle may have thus been established, but detailed predictions will naturally depend on the local situation.

5.8 Abandonment of coast

In the absence of restrictive factors, a full range of plant communities would be established at an appropriate distance landwards of their present positions. However, the present extent of salt marshes in, for example, Hamford Water, Essex, is at least partly dependent on sea defence measures, and, while theoretically transgression would result in the regeneration of the marshes further landwards, it is not certain to occur, especially if the higher predictions of sea level rise are fulfilled. It is distinctly possible that, at least in the next 50–100 years, salt marsh may become restricted to a fringe around the higher ground.

Changes in mud flat invertebrates

6.1 Distribution of intertidal invertebrates

Intertidal invertebrates usually occur in more or less distinct zones down the beach and within estuaries, although they can all live permanently submerged in areas such as the Baltic Sea, so tidal innundation, as such, is not important for most species. It does, however, determine the time available for filter feeders to feed and can, therefore, influence their growth and survival. The distribution of most species is probably determined by a combination of several factors, including the grain size of the sediment, organic content, salinity and exposure. Anderson (1972), Smyth *et al.* (1974), Kay and Knights (1975) and Wolff (1973) have all carried out multivariate analyses of invertebrate survey data and these physical variables, for various estuaries, and have described similar patterns,

Evans (1965) described a series of sediment zones for the Wash, some or all of which may be present at any one site, from the top of the beach to the low water mark.

(a) *Hydrobia ulvae, Nereis diversicolor* and *Corophium volutata* form an 'upper mud flat' group. Though few species are found in this zone, they are often very abundant and the area is very productive.

(b) The fine silty 'upper sand flats' with *Macoma balthica.*

(c) The well-sorted, medium grade, '*Arenicola* sand flats'. In addition to the lugworm, cockle *(Cerastoderma edule)* beds are usually found in this zone.

(d) The 'lower mud flats' may contain such species as the king ragworm *(Nereis virens),* or, in the absence of this or other predators, the same species found in the upper mud flats. Mussel *(Mytilus edulis)* beds are also common in this zone.

(e) The 'lower sand flats' occur below the level of low water of neap tides and consist of the coarsest sand. The tube worm *(Lanice conchilega)* and the bivalve mollusc *Tellina tenuis* are typical inhabitants.

6.2 Changes on open coasts and large estuaries

With no sea walls or other barriers to the sea, it is thought that the shore would move inland, retaining more or less existing profiles and proportions of different sediments. The rate of change may be important. Because, in general, the changes would be slow in relation to the life cycles of the invertebrates, the fauna overall is unlikely to show any changes other than 'normal' population fluctuations.

However, eroding sediments usually have poor faunas compared with areas of deposition, presumably because the larvae have difficulties in settling. Also, at points where there is high rapid erosion or a local concentration of erosion, eg high-level salt marsh eroding to mud mounds and mud flats, there may be a time lag between the effective loss of one habitat and the establishment of another.

6.3 Changes in narrow protected estuaries

In estuaries and harbours protected from vigorous wave action by narrow entrances, the dominant sedimentary process is deposition. Fine particles, eroded from open coast areas, are deposited on the mud flats raising their level, so that low-level flats are eventually replaced by high-level flats. This process would lead to an increase in such species as *Hydrobia ulvae* and *Nereis diversicolor* at the expense of, for example, *Macoma balthica* and *Nephtys hombergii.* Unless the sediments are polluted, they should remain rich productive areas until they reach a level at which they are not covered by high water of neap tides, when they would dry out, or they are colonized by plants and become salt marsh. In either case, the fauna is reduced and becomes seasonal.

Given an adequate supply of sediment, such areas would ultimately become filled with salt marsh and the only remaining mud flats would be the banks of the drainage creeks and channels. If the sediment supply is insufficient to counter the soil settlement and compaction in the upper marsh and to maintain its level, then the vegetation would die and there may be cycles of erosion and deposition. In any case, it is expected that, as the sea level rises, the entrance would eventually be widened by erosion or the protective bar overtopped. The estuary would then become open and erosion would be the dominant process.

6.4 Present sea walls raised

Where there are sea walls, it is expected that a rise in sea level would lead to a number of changes with consequences for the intertidal fauna. The beaches would become narrower, which would lead to a reduction in the absolute abundance of invertebrates, as the area of ground that species can occupy between the vertical limits would be reduced.

With the effective lowering of the beaches, salt marshes, with their mixture of marine and terrestrial faunas, would be eroded and eventually lost (Section 5.4). The same would be true for the upper mud flats. Species which prefer lower beach levels would be favoured, but in several species, eg *Arenicola marina* and *Macoma balthica,* the larvae settle in siltier sediments at a higher beach level than the adults occupy. The loss of the upper mud flats could, therefore, adversely affect these species. The general lowering of the beach levels might cause a downshore shift in the population of some species with a wide range, eg cockles *(Cerastoderma edule),* resulting in a proportional decrease in exposure time to bird predation, but increased time for feeding, so that individuals would grow bigger and/or fatter. This effect would be counteracted by the effect of changes in the nature of the sediments.

As the proportion of fine particles in the sediment is reduced by erosion, there would be a corresponding reduction in the organic matter content of the sediment (Wolff 1973). This decrease would lead, in turn, to a reduction in the productivity of deposit-feeding invertebrates, eg *Arenicola marina* (Longbottom 1970).

As the reduction in fine particles and organic matter proceeds, suspension feeders would become more important, with the decline of the deposit feeders. However, as the concentration of silt and clay particles continues to rise, animals would stop feeding before their filtration mechanisms become blocked (Widdows, Fieth & Worrall 1979), resulting in poor growth or an absence of suspension feeders, as in the Severn estuary.

A high sediment load also severely restricts light penetration into the water and reduces the phytoplankton production; again, the Severn is the classic example. This would not only severely restrict the growth of suspension feeders, but would probably also lead to a more general reduction of productivity in inshore waters.

If there is a gradual change from muddier to sandier sediments, then there might be several changes of species, for example:

Muddy	Intermediate	Sandy
Nereis diversicolor	*Nephtys hombergii*	*Nephtys cirrosa*
		N. longosetosa
Abra	*Macoma*	*Nucula*
Scrobicularia	*Cerastoderma*	*Tellina*
Mya		
Corophium	*C.arenarium*	*B. sarsi*
volutator	*Bathyporeia pilosa*	*Urothoe poseidonis*
		Haustorius arenarius

In the Wash, the building of a sea wall around part of the marsh has been quickly followed by an extension of the remaining marsh and the upper mud flats, as muddy sediments are deposited over the upper and/or *Arenicola* sand flats. If, when erosion occurs, this layer is simply stripped off the underlying sand, then it may be recolonized quickly by adult migration from lower levels or by larval recruitment.

However, fine sand particles are the most easily moved by water currents. Coarser sands are made of heavier particles, and fine-grained silt and clay sediments are cohesive, requiring stronger currents to erode and move them into suspension. It seems likely, therefore, that any water current or wave, with sufficient velocity or force to exceed the threshold value and erode the silt and clay particles, would also remove the fine sand particles. The result could be not a gradual change of sediment grade and of the animals living in it, but a rapid jump from fine clay and silt to medium/coarse sand, and consequently a much greater disturbance to, and change in, the fauna.

As a result of erosion, the surface of the sediment becomes increasingly covered in 'lag deposits' (shells, stones, etc). If sufficiently deep, this layer may give some measure of protection to the underlying fine sediments and slow down the process of erosion. Such areas may have good populations of shellfish and worms, but often only a limited number of species. Sediments consisting only of coarse particles, whether they are sand, shells or stones, have very poor faunas, because of the grinding action of the particles when moved by waves and currents.

Ultimately, if continued, erosion would leave only a hard clay base or the bed rock. The former supports only a few burrowing animals, eg piddocks *(Pholas dactylus),* and the latter would probably only develop a poor rocky shore fauna, because of periodic inundation by mobile sediments and 'sand blasting'.

Taken to its conclusion, open coasts would have only coarse unproductive sediments or hard substrates. A greater proportion of estuaries would also become marine and sandy, and the brackish section, with its very productive mud flats, would be reduced in area and located further inland and up-river.

The situation in the sheltered estuaries would initially be very different. Eroded sediments from open areas would be redeposited, extending and raising the mud flats and salt marshes. However, this process would only continue as long as the sediment supply was adequate. As the high rates of sedimentation decrease, there would first be cycles of erosion and deposition, and then erosion would become the dominant process, as on the open coasts.

6.5   New sea walls constructed landwards

If the new sea walls were constructed sufficiently far inland, the shore would simply migrate landwards, and the habitats would remain as at present. However, there could be complications to this process, as discussed in Sections 6.2 and 6.3. If the sea walls are rebuilt not as far inland, then the situation would be intermediate between the former situation and that described in Section 6.4.

6.6   Storm surge barriers built across estuaries

These barriers are operated in such a way that the tidal range is reduced. They also provide protection from waves. The combined effect produces a more sheltered, lower energy, system in which the accretion of fine particles can occur. Similar conditions are found in such areas as Poole Harbour, where, in addition to the usual mud flat species, there are a number of species only found in more sheltered areas, eg a number of species of the bivalve mollusc *Abra* and many species of sedentary tube worms. There is the danger, however, in these areas that organic enrichment will lead to a fauna dominated by small opportunist worms, or that green algal mats will develop causing anaerobic conditions at the sediment surface which will kill the in-fauna. Given an adequate supply of sediment, these areas would proceed as described in Section 6.3. They would eventually be dominated by salt marsh, protected behind the barrier.

6.7 Impermeable barriers built across estuaries

The survival of any of the marine invertebrates would depend on the maintenance of a sufficiently high salinity. Brackish lakes would retain some of the typical marine species, but with much reduced populations. A further decrease in salinity would cause the progressive loss of marine species, and allow their replacement by their fresh water counterparts. The processes involved have been well documented by studies on the brackish and fresh water lakes created by the Dutch Delta Works (Saeijs 1982).

6.8   Abandonment of coast

This option would result in the movement of the present zones landwards, the classic transgression described in Sections 4.6 and 5.8. The effect on the invertebrate populations has been outlined in Sections 6.2 and 6.3.

Changes in bird populations

7.1 Birds of salt marshes

A number of species nest in salt marshes, including waders (notably redshank *(Tringa totanus)*, oyster-catcher *(Haematopus ostralegus)*, lapwing *(Vanellus vanellus)*, ringed plover *(Charadrius hiaticula)*, and, occasionally in northern Britain, curlew *(Numenius arquata)* and dunlin *(Calidris alpina)*, gulls (notably the black-headed gull *(Larus ridibundus)*), some terns (such as the common tern *(Sterna hirundo)*), wildfowl (eg mallard *(Anas platyrhynchos)* and the shelduck *(Tadorna tadorna)*), and a number of passerines (eg skylark *(Alauda arvensis)*, reed bunting *(Emberiza schoeniclus)* and meadow pipit *(Anthus pratensis)*).

Amongst all these species, salt marshes are generally regarded as being the most important for the redshank, which, in a recent survey of the breeding birds of the British marshes (Cadbury, Green & Allport 1987), was found to nest at considerably higher densities than those found in any of the inland breeding sites of this species. The same survey revealed that the redshank occurred at the highest densities in marshes with the greatest variety of salt marsh plants. This finding probably reflects a preference for those marshes with a large range in height because, like all salt marsh species that nest on the ground, the nests are vulnerable to flooding at high spring tides (Hale 1980). The birds nest in the middle and upper levels of the marsh to reduce the risk of their nests being inundated. The survey also showed that, whereas latitude had no effect on breed-ing density, redshank densities were higher in the east of the country than in the west. This factor was perhaps associated with the level of grazing on the different marshes; redshank densities were highest on marshes subjected to a medium level of grazing.

The total number of redshank nesting in Britain's 3820 ha of salt marsh was calculated as 17 500 pairs, some 60% of the 30 000-34 000 pairs estimated to breed in

Britain (Cadbury *et al.* 1987). Of those nesting on salt marsh, approximately 50% nested in East Anglia, where one-third of Britain's salt marshes occur. The salt marshes in north-west Britain were the next most important.

Some waders feed in the marsh creeks and muddy patches, notably the redshank and grey plover *(Pluvialis squatarola)*. Many wildfowl graze in the marsh, notably the brent goose *(Branta bernicla)* and the wigeon *(Anas penelope)*. These birds tend to forage in the grazed areas. Several passerines also forage in the salt marsh, and for the twite *(Acanthis flavirostris)* salt marsh is its main habitat. According to the study by Davies (1987) on the Wash, reed buntings preferred the coarser vegetation communities at the higher levels of the marsh, whereas rock pipits *(Anthus spinoletta)* and skylarks were widely scattered. The twites were found primarily in the marsh samphire and sea aster zones at the lower levels of the marsh.

7.2 Birds of mud flats

Many bird species exploit the invertebrates that live in and on the intertidal sediments. They include a number of species of wildfowl (notably the shelduck and the eider duck *(Somateria mollissima)*), several species of gulls (notably the black-headed gull) and about 20 species of wading birds. Concern focuses most on those species for which estuaries are the main source of food, and these include the shelduck and most waders. Although some of these species breed in the vicinity of the British shoreline in the summer, most of them occur in their greatest numbers outside the breeding season. Large numbers are present on migra-tion between their breeding and wintering grounds during late summer, autumn and in the spring. In addition, many of them spend either the whole winter on the British shore or go there when severe conditions further to the north and east drive them from their main

Sea grass (Zostera marina), *the food of the brent goose*

Brent geese (Brenta bernicla) *at Leigh Marsh, Essex*

wintering areas, such as the Waddenzee. It has been estimated that British estuaries act as a wintering area for more than one-half of Europe's waders (Hale 1980).

Some wildfowl (notably the brent goose and wigeon) also feed in winter on the vegetation, macroalgae and seagrass, living on the surface of the intertidal flats.

Whether carnivorous or herbivorous, the abundance of the food supply varies both along and down the shore. The particle size distribution, stability, exposure time and organic content of the sediments are all thought to affect the abundance of these food organisms (Section 6.1).

Therefore, the water level on the shore affects the abundance of the various food organisms available, which, in turn, affects where the birds feed. There are well-established relationships, at various levels of scale, relating bird density to food abundance (Goss-Custard 1985).

There is increasing evidence that competition between birds limits the numbers that can use a particular estuary, or part of it (Goss-Custard 1985). As bird density increases, the various forms of interference that occur between birds as they forage become more intense, and the rate at which the prey is depleted also increases. The combined effect is that feeding conditions deteriorate as bird numbers rise. In herbivorous wildfowl, the birds regularly eat out their food supply in parts of their winter range and have to move on to other sources. In carnivorous waders and ducks, the birds are usually more dispersed and the rate of depletion of their food supply is less rapid (Goss-Custard & Charman 1976). Nevertheless, evidence from several species of waders suggests that, through interference, a given abundance of food can only carry a certain density of birds, and, for some species, many estuaries are already at capacity (Goss-Custard & Moser 1988; Moser 1988).

Food abundance is thought to interact with the time available for feeding to determine the numbers of birds that can be supported by a particular intertidal flat. The birds are only able to feed at low water, so the exposure time of the flat affects how long they can forage. When the feeding time is reduced because the upper levels of the beach have been removed by the spread of hybrid cordgrass (Goss-Custard & Moser 1988) or by reclamation for industrial purposes (Evans 1981), the numbers of some sensitive species (notably the dunlin) have decreased sharply in some estuaries.

Another factor thought to affect the number of birds using an intertidal flat for feeding is the width of the shore. Perhaps because many avian predators attack from the direction of the shore (Whitfield 1985), some waders seem to avoid narrow shores (Bryant 1979). Many wildfowl also avoid narrow shores, presumably because of the greater risk of disturbance from people.

7.3   Birds of inshore waters
A number of birds use the shallow inshore waters as fishing grounds during both the breeding and non-breeding season. Several species of terns, for example, breed around the British coast, and feed on small fish often taken quite close to the shore. Saw-billed ducks, such as the red-breasted merganser *(Mergus serrator)*, cormorants *(Phalacrocorax carbo)* and shags *(P. aristotelis)* all catch fish in inshore coastal waters.

7.4   Present sea walls raised
Even a rise in sea level of 0.8 m would result in the present upper marsh (GSM) changing to lower marsh. As this area is frequently inundated by the tide, it would be unsuitable for breeding birds. It is, therefore, likely that over 50% of the British breeding redshank would no longer be able to breed successfully on the salt marshes, especially as such a high proportion breed in the vulnerable south-east of England. With the drainage of inland wetland sites so far advanced, it is unlikely that the redshank would be able to find alternative breeding sites in Britain. The other species breeding on marshes would be much less affected, as rather small numbers are involved.

The birds feeding on the vegetation of the upper marsh would certainly be affected, especially the grazing wildfowl, such as the brent goose. The birds that feed on the vegetation of the lower marsh would be less affected, and might benefit from extra habitat resulting from the 0.8 m sea level rise. The higher sea level rises would seriously affect all marsh-feeding birds.

The changes in nature of the intertidal flats, anticipated here, would be disadvantageous for most of the birds. First, the abundance of many of the food organisms would be reduced because of the unfavourable change in the nature and stability of the sediments, the greater turbidity of the water (which is disadvantageous for plants, phytoplankton and suspension-feeding invertebrates), and the reduced productivity of inshore waters as a whole (Section 6.4). Second, the reduced width, and therefore area, of the shore would force birds to feed at higher densities, with a consequent increase in competition between them. Third, the reduced exposure time following the degradation of the flats would remove some of the time available for feeding. Finally, the narrower shores might increase the rates of predation on and disturbance to some vulnerable species.

Because waders are already thought to be dying from food shortage (Goss-Custard 1985), either through starvation or indirectly because hungry birds are easier for predators to catch, a further reduction in the quality of their feeding conditions would probably lead to a decrease in population size (Goss-Custard 1980). However, there are a few species for which the predicted changes could bring an increased food supply. The turnstone *(Arenaria interpres)* is the most likely species to benefit, because harder and coarser substrates, with the associated algae, provide places in which their prey can live.

The increased turbidity of the water would make it more difficult for the birds to catch fish in the inshore areas. Furthermore, the fish stocks themselves might be reduced by the increased turbidity and the stronger wave attack, which could directly affect the fish themselves or indirectly their food organisms.

7.5 New sea walls constructed landwards
So long as the new walls were constructed sufficiently far inland for new marshes to form (Sections 4.3 & 5.5), there should be no adverse effects on the populations of birds that breed or feed in the salt marshes or mud flats. The increased turbidity of inshore waters might, however, affect the birds feeding there, as described above (Section 7.4).

7.6 Storm surge barriers built across estuaries
The building of storm surge barriers could result in the development of extra salt marsh at the expense of mud flats (Sections 4.4 & 5.6), and this development could provide extra habitat for the birds that breed or feed in salt marshes. Clearly, however, much would depend on the kind of marsh that developed.

The birds feeding on mud flats would find it more difficult to collect sufficient food, because the reduced space would increase competition and there would be less time to feed. On the other hand, the finer and more stable deposits might increase the densities of some invertebrates, especially the suspension feeders. Predicting the net effect of these contradictory changes is difficult at present, but is being attempted in connection with the Severn barrage proposals.

The inshore waters inside the barrier would be expected to be less turbid and calmer, which should benefit the fish-eating birds. The waters outside the barrier might be deeper and more turbid than at present, so, if these areas are used, feeding might be more difficult in the vicinity of the barrier itself.

7.7 Impermeable barriers built across estuaries
With the loss of salt marshes (Sections 4.5 & 5.7), the birds that breed there at present would have to find alternative areas. Whether or not they do so would depend on the nature of the habitats within the barrier. These areas could be quite suitable for redshank breeding, but much would depend on the kind and extent of vegetation available, which, in turn, depends on the drainage and grazing regime. Most of the birds presently feeding in the salt marsh might be able to find food in these new habitats. The exception would be the twite; it is unlikely to find alternative feeding grounds.

The loss of the intertidal zone would remove the main food supplies of the birds feeding there at present. Few of them are likely to find alternative supplies inside the newly created habitats within the barriers. Wildfowl may be less affected than the waders. The removal of salt water within the barrier would also remove the species presently eaten by the birds feeding in shallow estuarine waters, and their success in adapting would depend on their ability to locate new sources of food.

7.8 Abandonment of coast
The effects on the bird populations are likely to be essentially as described in Section 7.5, which considered the effect of rebuilding sea walls further inland. There are likely to be some changes, at least on the local scale, but dramatic major effects are less likely.

Changes in sandy beaches, sand dunes and shingle beaches

8.1   Introduction

The principle of transgression that was applied to marshes and flats (Section 4.6) also applies, in general terms, to sandy beaches, sand dunes and shingle banks. The same qualification, namely the freedom of natural movement, also applies. In many cases, and for a variety of reasons, free natural movement cannot be permitted. There is the added question of the supply of material. Sites at present in active growth with an abundant supply of sand or shingle are much more likely to survive relatively unchanged than sites where there is a limited supply of new material. Most sand and shingle areas of conservation or amenity interest are at present either unprotected or only partially protected from natural marine erosion. It is unlikely that the measure of protection given can be increased very much except in special circumstances. Such a circumstance might be when the feature plays a major role in sea defence, eg where a low-lying coast is fronted by a line of high dunes, or where vital structures, eg a nuclear power station, would otherwise be threatened. Consideration will be given to each habitat type, rather than under the various sea defence options as in previous Sections.

8.2   Sandy beaches

The critical factors here are the supply of sand and the freedom of movement of the feature. For a beach backed by a sea wall, the rising sea level and the deepening water would increase erosion, resulting in a lowering of the beach. Not only would an important amenity be lost, but the stability of the sea wall itself would be threatened. Most bathing beaches are backed by a sea wall, and these beaches would be greatly reduced in area by sea level rise. High-level beaches would become lower level, and the characteristic strandline floras and faunas would be lost completely.

Where the beach is on an unprotected coast, the present beach would be eroded, but it is likely to be redeposited further inland, as described previously for salt marshes and mud flats. The net effects, in the long term, are likely to be quite small, as most of the organisms associated with the mobile habitats provided by sandy beaches could withstand the likely rates of change. However, there would be increased recreational pressure on such beaches because of the losses of amenity beaches protected by a sea wall as described above.

8.3   Sand dunes

Because of the wide range of types of sand formations that occur in the British Isles, it is difficult to generalize on the effects of sea level rise on sand dune habitats. Initially, there would be erosion, or increased erosion, of the seaward dune ridges. The sand released by this process, together with any sand reserves in the system, would then be available for new dune building along a line further landwards. The extent of this landward migration would depend on the sand supply offshore, the sand supply mobilized by dune erosion, the strength and direction of the prevailing winds, and the general physiography of the site. Many of the larger dune sites are likely to survive relatively unchanged, except for the loss of the coastal strip, the subsequent regeneration of primary dune communities, and some overall increase in dune mobility.

In some cases, such losses that occur may be offset by a beneficial effect of sea level rise. Sand dune systems have an underlying layer of fresh water floating on the sea water beneath. Many of the characteristic sand dune plant communities are restricted to areas where this fresh water layer is at or near the surface, the so-called dune slack communities (Boorman 1977, 1988). These communities are dynamic and are vulnerable to change. They can be lost by the accretion of extra sand, effectively lowering the water table, or they can be lost through a direct fall in the water table as a result of water extraction for the growth of trees, or by drainage of adjoining land used for agriculture or forestry. A major rise in sea level would cause a corresponding rise in the fresh water table, with the regeneration of dune slack communities.

While the relatively favourable possibilities above would apply to the small number of really large dune sites, there are very many important small dune sites where the natural adjustment would not, or could not, be allowed to take place. This situation would apply both to sites reduced in size by residential or industrial development, and to sites limited in size by natural features, such as cliff foot sites. For many of these sites, a rise in sea level of the magnitude predicted could cause major losses of habitat that would in no

Active mobile sand dunes on both sides of the mouth of the River Ythan, Aberdeenshire

way be offset by the favourable changes outlined above. However, the integration of the requirements of dune reinforcement for sea defence and for dune ecosystem management can help considerably to reduce undesirable changes (de Jong & Visser 1983).

8.4   Shingle beaches

The same general principles regarding the necessity of space for freedom of movement, if natural compensatory processes are to be effective, apply also to shingle beaches. There are a few large shingle structures where transgressional adjustment could compensate for sea level rise, with little overall change. At Dungeness, a rise in sea level would further increase erosion along the south shore, but this would be compensated for by increased deposition along the east shore with little overall loss in conservation value. The process would probably not be allowed to take place, however, because of the nuclear power stations close to the south shore. Other constraints apply to the various other shingle areas that are adjacent to residential or commercial developments.

Shingle spits such as Orfordness have a long history of cyclical changes, periods of building alternating with periods of erosion, and a major rise in sea level would reinforce present erosive tendencies. If there are artificial restraints to the natural processes, necessary sea defence works would affect the biological and physiographic interest of the site, in addition to the expense involved in protecting these formations as they stand.

The changes in water table described for sand dunes would also apply to the larger shingle beaches. It is difficult to predict the magnitude of the effect. A small increase is likely to be favourable, restoring water levels reduced by water abstraction, but larger increases could lead to the creation of extra fresh or brackish water habitats, at the expense of terrestrial habitats.

The relatively narrow shingle beaches found especially on high-energy coasts in the west and north should survive relatively unchanged, except for some steepening and landwards movement. The associated flora of these storm beaches should be able to withstand the changes.

The shingle bank at Walberswick, Suffolk, is being forced shorewards over the salt marshes behind

Changes in earth cliffs

9.1 Direct effects

The major areas of earth cliffs, such as those in Norfolk and north Humberside, are already subject to major erosive losses. The postulated rises in sea level would increase the depth of water offshore; larger waves would be able to reach the cliff foot, with a consequent increase in the rates of erosion. The biological effects would be quite small, but the social implications of a further increase in the rates of erosion would be considerable.

9.2 Indirect consequences

If the increased erosion of the earth cliffs was permitted to occur unchecked, the areas receiving the sediment removed from the cliffs would benefit considerably. The sediment made available would enable natural processes to compensate for rises in sea level. If, however, the losses along the cliff coast were halted or reduced by coastal protection measures, the consequences for the former receiving areas would be enormous, with major losses of habitat, to say nothing of the sea defence problems created.

Soft cliffs of glacial sand and gravel at Mundesley, Norfolk, are readily eroded by the sea

Changes in the paramaritime zone

The paramaritime zone can be defined as the area landwards of the coast itself, where there is still a discernible maritime influence on the natural fauna and flora. The width of this zone depends on the lie of the land and on the strength of the onshore winds. Along the exposed coasts of the north and west, an increase in the maritime influence would be limited by high ground, although the combined effect of a higher sea level coupled with stormier conditions could considerably extend this paramaritime zone. In the low-lying areas of the south-east a rise in sea level could significantly increase the landwards penetration of the marine and maritime influence in several different ways.

The rivers of Norfolk, Suffolk and Cambridgeshire are already at capacity and flood more or less regularly at certain times of the year. With the combination of an anticipated 20% increase in rainfall and the predicted rise in sea level, there is likely to be a major increase in the extent and frequency of such flooding. The biological effects would depend on the water management policies adopted. Present 'wash lands', that are flooded by the storage of excess water in the winter but used extensively by breeding birds in the summer, could be lost as a result of near permanent flooding, but they might be replaced by the incorporation of new areas similarly used for the storage of excess water in the winter.

In addition to the increased threat of flooding, the East Anglian rivers would also experience more frequently, and to a greater extent, the salt penetration that caused the major fish kill in Broadland last year. Such an event, previously experienced only a few times in a hundred years, might become a more or less regular occurrence. As a result, long stretches of the rivers and most of the Broads would become increasingly brackish, with corresponding effects on the flora and fauna. The penetration of sea water inland through permeable sands and gravels, already experienced on a limited scale in east Norfolk, would increase further.

In the event of new sea defence and coast protection strategies, such as the building of major barrages or tidal flood barriers, changes to the environment and natural habitats could extend many miles inland.

Hickling Broad, Norfolk. There is already a detectable marine influence in some of the eastern broads, of which Hickling is typical

Distribution of changes in the United Kingdom

All parts of the British Isles would experience some effect from a change in sea level of the magnitude predicted. The largest changes would, however, be in the south and east, particularly from the Humber to Poole Habour, and in other major estuaries such as the Severn, the Mersey, Morecambe Bay and the Solway (Figure 1). The various sites of amenity or conservation interest are all inter-related. Changes in one site would have its effects on other sites; studies made in one area would be significant for others. Many, if not most, of the bird species move, more or less freely, between the various areas in Britain, as well as those of nearby mainland Europe. It is clear that all the studies in the British Isles should be co-ordinated and, moreover, close links should be established with studies on the corresponding, and inter-related, changes that would take place on the other side of the North Sea, in the Netherlands, and in France, Belgium and Germany. The changes experienced in the Netherlands, following the building of the Delta Works, will provide vital background information in preparation for the changes likely to be experienced during the coming decades.

Socio-economic considerations

There are already many conflicting demands on our coastal resources. These demands include the needs of sea defence, industrial developments, amenity and recreation, and nature conservation. All of these uses will be brought into further conflict as a result of the changes caused by rising sea level.

Along undefended coasts, the natural compensatory movements of coastal deposits and their associated ecosystems will bring about new conflicts of land use. Along shorelines protected by sea walls, present conflicts will be greatly increased as the coastal zones are narrowed or destroyed. New sea defence options will each have their own environmental problems. Relocation of the sea wall landwards will invariably cause a range of socio-economic problems, as this development will affect not only agricultural land but also homes or even whole communities. The building of

major estuarine barriers, as well as being very expensive, will create new habitats, but also new problems.

However, there are yet further complications. The rise in sea level is only one of the consequences of a global climatic warming. It is predicted that much of England will experience a climate closer to that of south-west France today. The more favourable climate will certainly encourage all forms of coastal recreation. These extra demands will be particularly difficult to meet at a time when decreasing coastal resources will come under increasing pressures from all sides.

The best that we can do is, first, to predict as accurately as possible the likely changes, and then to formulate integrated plans to ensure the optimum use of our coastal resources, including the design of new techniques for integrated management.

Research requirements

The following is a general outline of the areas of study that would be necessary for a detailed assessment of the effects of sea level rise on the fauna and flora and for the formulation of appropriate techniques to minimize the impact of such effects. Some of the details would be affected by the choices of sea defence strategy, but broad outlines are indicated.

The research proposals are grouped, under each general subject heading, into four categories (A–D) based on their relative urgency. First, there are the primary projects, category A, concerned with providing the background information needed to forecast, in detail, the changes caused by specific rises in sea level. Second come the projects, category B, concerned with the forecasting and interpretation of the consequences of such changes. Third are the category C projects concerned with the implication of specific sea defence schemes and the associated problems of coastal zone management. Finally, there are the long-term, category D, projects associated with the ecological monitoring and coastal zone management that will be required as the rises actually occur.

The first two categories are for immediate consideration, but category A will partly depend on results from category B and thus could well begin 2–4 years after the initial start. The timing of category C projects would depend on the formulation of specific sea defence policies, with research funding needed in the 5–10 year period. The need for category D projects would be greatest in the 10–15 year period.

12.1 Research on physical processes
CATEGORY A
Studies on the effect of predicted sea level rises on beach processes, sediment sorting and transport, and on patterns of erosion and accretion, especially in the most vulnerable coastal areas of mud flats, salt marshes, shingle banks and sand dunes.

CATEGORY C
Model studies on changes in erosion and deposition, and the effect on sediment transport in, and between, the various estuaries under the different sea defence options in particular areas.

12.2 Salt marsh research
CATEGORY A
Studies on the tidal requirements of the various salt marsh plant communities and their ability to respond to changing conditions.

Surveys of the distribution of salt marsh plant species and plant communities to determine the magnitude and nature of the changes consequent on predicted sea level rises.

CATEGORY B
Studies on changes in the ability of salt marsh plant species to stabilize and hold marsh sediments under unfavourable conditions.

Studies on the effect of sediment type, including the effect of pollutants, on the establishment and growth of salt marsh plants.

Studies on techniques for the rapid re-establishment of salt marsh plant species on new areas of mud flats and management techniques for achieving particular salt marsh plant communities.

Studies on environmental factors, other than sea level, that can affect salt marsh growth and development adversely, including the effects of eutrophication and of specific pollutants.

CATEGORY C
Studies on the changes in distribution of salt marsh plants and plant communities consequent on the reduction in tidal influence resulting from the construction of tidal barriers.

CATEGORY D
Survey and monitoring of the changes in plant species and plant communities consequent upon sea level rise.

12.3 Invertebrate research
CATEGORY A
Studies on the relationship between invertebrate biomass and productivity and beach width, beach level, sediment type, and sediment organic content.

CATEGORY B
Studies on the relative importance of pelagic and benthic micro-organisms and organic matter as food for different intertidal invertebrates, including experimental studies comparing different estuaries with different sediment loads.

Studies on the development of faunas in relation to changes in habitat and sediment type, including the effect of pollutants.

CATEGORY C
Studies on the effect of shelter and exposure on the species composition and biomass of intertidal faunas, with special reference to the creation and management of replacement habitats for wading birds and wildfowl.

CATEGORY D
Survey and monitoring of the changes in biomass and productivity of invertebrates consequent upon sea level rise.

12.4 Bird research

CATEGORY A
Studies on the distribution of birds that breed on salt marshes, particularly the redshank, and their breeding success, at different levels of the marsh. The objective would be to calculate the proportion of nests that would be at risk from sea level rises of different degrees.

Studies on birds feeding on salt marshes in relation to level and vegetation type, to identify those species most vulnerable to changes in the salt marshes.

CATEGORY B
A survey of eroding and non-eroding coasts in the south-east of England in order to develop a model relating the numbers of birds using a shore to its width, erosion status and sediment type. Such a model would be used to predict how expected changes in these variables might affect the numbers of each species using a shore.

Studies on the importance of inshore coastal waters to fish-eating birds. The results could be used to predict how bird numbers might be affected by predicted changes in water depth, water turbidity and the nature of bottom sediments.

CATEGORY C
Studies on the recolonization of flooded coastal meadows to determine the possibilities of creating new habitat for birds displaced by losses of former marsh areas.

Information review supplemented by ground surveys of breeding and feeding habitats inland, but adjacent to the coast, in order to establish the vegetation types that might be most favoured by birds currently breeding or feeding on the salt marsh.

Information review supplemented by ground surveys of habitats inshore of coastal barriers in order to determine their use by birds that normally feed on coastal flats and in shallow inshore waters.

CATEGORY D
Survey and monitoring of coastal bird populations in relation to sea level rise and associated habitat changes.

12.5 Other research

CATEGORY A
Studies on the effects of sea level rise on sand dune systems and sand dune habitats, including changing erosion patterns, the regeneration of habitat, changes in water tables, and the effects on dune flora and fauna.

Studies on the effect of sea level rise on the flora and fauna of shingle deposits, especially in relation to erosion patterns and water table changes.

CATEGORY B
Studies to assess the long-term effects of changes in dune and shingle habitats, and to devise suitable management techniques for minimizing the losses of species and habitats.

Socio-economic studies on the interaction between ecological changes on the coast and the changing pattern of recreational activities in the coastal zone.

CATEGORY C
Case studies of the ecological impacts of major sea defence, industrial, recreational or other projects on sandy beaches, sand dunes, and shingle banks.

CATEGORY D
Survey and monitoring of changes in sandy beach, sand dune and shingle habitats, and of the changing patterns in the use and exploitation of the coastal zone in relation to the rising sea levels.

References

ANDERSON, S.S 1972. The ecology of Morecambe Bay. II. Intertidal invertebrates and factors affecting their distribution. *Journal of Applied Ecology*, **9**, 161–178.

ANON. 1986. *Zeespiegelrijzing – worstelen met wassend water.* Middleburg: Rijkswaterstaat.

BEEFTINK, W.G. 1979. The structure of salt marsh communities in relation to environmental disturbances. In: *Ecological processes in coastal environments*, edited by R.L. Jeffrey & A.J. Davy, 77–93. Oxford: Blackwell Scientific.

BOORMAN, L.A. 1977. Sand dunes. In: *The coastline*, edited by R.S.K. Barnes, 161–197. London: Wiley.

BOORMAN, L.A. 1987. *A survey of salt marsh erosion along the Essex coast.* (Natural Environment Research Council contract report to the Anglian Water Authority.) Abbots Ripton: Institute of Terrestrial Ecology. (Unpublished)

BOORMAN, L.A. 1988. The sand dunes of Britain. In: *Dry coastal ecosystems*, edited by E. van der Maarel. Amsterdam: Elsevier.

BRYANT, D.M. 1979. Effects of prey density and site characteristics on estuary usage by overwintering waders (Charadrii). *Estuarine, Coastal and Marine Science*, **9**, 369–385.

BUTLER, R.J. 1978. *Salt marsh morphology and the evolution of Colne Point in Essex, England.* PhD thesis, Queen Mary College, London.

CADBURY, C.J., GREEN, R.E. & ALLPORT, G. 1987. Redshank and other breeding waders of British salt marshes. *RSPB Conservation Review*, no. 1, 37–40.

CARTER, D.J.T. & DRAPER, I. 1988. Has the north-east Atlantic become rougher? *Nature*, **337**, 494.

DAVIES, M. 1987. Twite and other wintering passerines on the Wash salt marshes. In: *The Wash and its environment*, edited by P. Doody & B. Barrett, 123–132. (Research and survey in nature conservation no. 7.) Peterborough: Nature Conservancy Council.

EVANS, G. 1965. Intertidal flat sediments and their environments of deposition in the Wash. *Quarterly Journal of the Geological Society of London*, **121**, 209–245.

EVANS, P.R. 1981. Reclamation of intertidal land: some effects on shelduck and wader populations in the Tees estuary. *Verhandlungen der Ornithologischen Gesellschaft in Bayern*, **23**, 147–168.

FLATHER, R.A. & KHANDKER, H. 1987. A storm surge problem and possible effects of sea level changes on coastal flooding in the Bay of Bengal. *Int. Workshop on climate change, sea level, severe tropical storms, and associated impacts, September 1987, Norwich.* (Unpublished)

GOSS-CUSTARD, J.D. 1980. Competition for food and interference among waders. *Ardea*, **68**, 31–52.

GOSS-CUSTARD, J.D. 1985. Foraging behaviour of wading birds and the carrying capacity of estuaries. In: *Behavioural ecology: ecological consequences of adaptive behaviour*, edited by R.M. Sibly & R.H. Smith, 169–188. Oxford: Blackwell Scientific.

GOSS-CUSTARD, J.D. & CHARMAN, K. 1976. Predicting how many wintering waterfowl an area can support. *Wildfowl*, **27**, 157–158.

GOSS-CUSTARD, J.D. & MOSER, M.E. 1988. Rates of change in the numbers of dunlin *Calidris alpina* wintering in British estuaries in relation to the spread of *Spartina anglica*. *Journal of Applied Ecology*, **25**, 95–109.

GROENENDIJK, A.M. 1983. Tidal management: the consequences for the salt marsh vegetation. *Water Science and Technology*, **16**, 79–86.

GROENENDIJK, A.M. 1985. Ecological consequences of tidal management for the salt marsh vegetation. In: *Ecology of coastal vegetation*, edited by W.G. Beeftink, J. Rozema & A.H.L. Huiskes, 415–424. Dordrecht: Junk.

HALE, W.G. 1980. *Waders.* (New Naturalist series.) London: Collins.

HARMSWORTH, G.C. & LONG, S.P. 1986. An assessment of salt marsh erosion in Essex, England, with reference to the Dengie peninsula. *Biological Conservation*, **35**, 377–387.

HOFFMAN, J.S. 1984. Estimates of future sea level rise. In: *The greenhouse effect and sea level rise*, edited by M.C. Barth & J.G. Titus, 79–103. New York: Van Nostrand Reinhold.

JONG, G.J. de & VISSER J. 1983. Environmental aspects of reinforcements in coastal dune areas. *Water Science and Technology*, **16**, 377–386.

KAY, D.G. & KNIGHTS, R.D. 1975. The macro-invertebrate fauna of the intertidal soft sediments of south-east England. *Journal of the Marine Biological Association of the United Kingdom*, **55**, 811–832.

KIRBY, R. 1969. *Sedimentary environments, sedimentary processes and river history in the lower Medway, Kent.* PhD thesis, Queen Mary College, London.

LONGBOTTOM, M.R. 1970. The distribution of *Arenicola marina* (L.) with particular reference to the effects of particle size and organic matter in the sediments. *Journal of Experimental Marine Biology and Ecology*, **5**, 138–157.'

MOSER, M.E. 1988. Limits to the numbers of grey plovers (*Pluvialis squatarola*) wintering on British estuaries: an analysis of long term population trends. *Journal of Applied Ecology*, **25**, 473–485.

PIRAZZOLI, P.A. 1986. Secular trends of relative sea level changes indicated by tide gauge records. *Journal of Coastal Research*, **1**, 1–26.

ROBIN, G. de Q. 1986. Changing the sea level. In: *The greenhouse effect, climatic change and ecosystems*, edited by B. Bolin, B. Doos, J. Jager & R.A. Warrick. (SCOPE 29.) Chichester: Wiley.

SAEIJS, H.L.F. 1982. *Changing estuaries.* PhD thesis, Rijksuniversiteit, Leiden.

SALINAS, L.M., DELAUNE, R. & PATRICK, W.H. 1986. Changes occurring along a rapidly submerging coastal area: Louisiana, USA. *Journal of Coastal Research*, **2**, 269–284.

SMYTH, J.C., CURTIS, D.J., GIBSON, I. & WILKINSON, M. 1974, Intertidal organisms of an industrialised estuary. *Marine Pollution Bulletin*, **5**, 188–191.

WHITFIELD, D.P. 1985. Raptor predation on wintering waders in south eastern Scotland. *Ibis*, **127**, 544–558.

WIDDOWS, J., FIETH, P. & WORRALL, C.M. 1979. Relationships between seston, available food and feeding activity in the common mussel, *Mytilus edulis* (L.). *Marine Biology*, **50**, 195–208.

WOLFF, W.J. 1973. The estuary as a habitat. An analysis of the data on soft-bottomed macrofauna of the estuarine areas of the rivers Rhine, Meuse and Scheldt. *Zoologische Verhandelingen*, **126**, 1–242.

Printed in the United Kingdom for Her Majesty's Stationery Office
Dd291020 C25 5/89 3936 12521